DISNEY

Christopher Robin

The Little Book of POOH-isms

With help from PIGLET, EEYORE, RABBIT, OWL, and TIGGER, too!

centum

As told to Brittany Rubiano

Art by Mike Wall

CHRISTOPHER ROBIN: THE LITTLE BOOK OF POOH-ISMS
A CENTUM BOOK 9781912564514
Published in Great Britain by Centum Books Ltd
This edition published 2018
1 3 5 7 9 10 8 6 4 2

Centum Books Ltd, 20 Devon Square, Newton Abbot, Devon,
TQ12 2HR, UK
books@centumbooksltd.co.uk
CENTUM BOOKS Limited Reg. No. 07641486
A CIP catalogue record for this book is available from the
British Library
Printed in Italy

ADVENTURES

CHRISTOPHER ROBIN: Come on, Pooh.

POOH: Where are we going, Christopher Robin?

CHRISTOPHER ROBIN: Nowhere.

POOH: One of my favourite places.

Adventures to Nowhere are some of the greatest.

"If it's not Here,
that means
it's out There."

—WINNIE THE POOH

*Comforting words when one
has lost something important,
like a key or a sock.*

"Tiggers
never get lost."

—TIGGER

*It's a known fact that tiggers
are better than compasses.*

"I always get to where
I am going by walking
away from where
I have been."

—WINNIE THE POOH

*Quests are funny things
that way.*

"Hello, there.
Are you on an
expotition,
too?"

—WINNIE THE POOH

*You never know whom
you might meet on your travels.*

"Sometimes if I am going Somewhere and I wait, Somewhere comes to me."

—WINNIE THE POOH

Somewhere is often just around the corner.

"We keep looking for home, but we keep finding this pit. I thought if we start looking for this pit, we might find home."

—WINNIE THE POOH

The best path is not always the most obvious one.

"Oh, boy, it's good to be home."

—PIGLET

Coming home can be one of the nicest parts of the journey.

HUNDRED-ACRE WISDOM

"You are braver than you believe, stronger than you seem and smarter than you think."

—CHRISTOPHER ROBIN

Always remember. . . .

"Can't change the inevitable, just have to go with the flow."

—EEYORE

It might bring a nice change of scenery.

"It's worth a t-t-try."

—PIGLET

A good attitude is everything.

"You can't **sneeze**
without knowing it."

—WINNIE THE POOH

Quite true.

"Never trust that thing between your ears. Brains will get you nowhere fast, my dears. Haven't had a need for mine in years. On the page is where the truth appears."

—RABBIT

Hmmm . . . this could be what the Heffalumps and Woozles want you to believe. Best to keep reading and thinking.

"Think, think, think."

—WINNIE THE POOH

When in doubt . . .

"A little consideration makes all the difference."

—EEYORE

Noticing goes a long way.

"The time has come to speak plainly."

—PIGLET

Communication is key.

"If people are upset because you've forgotten something, console them by letting them know you didn't forget – you just weren't remembering."

—WINNIE THE POOH

Whoops.

"Ah, yes. I see it.
Quite clear. Never
really doubted it at all."

—OWL

*It's okay to admit when you
stand corrected.*

"We all have our little ways."

—EEYORE

And some of us have our big ways, too.

"A weather vane is not a Heffalump!"

—RABBIT

It can be hard to tell – always good to make sure.

"I wonder what's going to happen **exciting** today."

—PIGLET

A positive outlook turns a blustery day into a hummy one.

"Think of all the possibilities."

—EEYORE

There are many!

FRIENDSHIP

CHRISTOPHER ROBIN: I've changed tremendously.

POOH: Not right here. It's still you looking out.

A true friend always knows.

"It's so much more friendly with two."

—PIGLET

That goes for everything from shelf-reaching to smackerel-eating.

"Thanks for happenin' to pass me."

—EEYORE

Impromptu visits can brighten one's day.

"I shouldn't care to say AHA! by myself."

—PIGLET

Some aha's are meant to be shared.

"That's what I call a Friendly Day."

—WINNIE THE POOH

And a day well spent, at that!

CHRISTOPHER ROBIN: Pooh, promise you won't forget about me. Not even when I'm a hundred.

POOH: How old shall I be then?

CHRISTOPHER ROBIN: Ninety-nine.

Forever friendships are the best sort.

TIME

"It's usually today."

—WINNIE THE POOH

You can always check your
Pooh-koo clock to make sure.

"Here today and gone tomorrow."

—EEYORE

What a difference a day makes.

"What's wrong with knowing what you know now and not knowing what you don't know now until later?"

—WINNIE THE POOH

Indeed, until the unknown becomes the known, best not to worry.

"Yesterday, when it was tomorrow, it was too exciting a day for me."

—WINNIE THE POOH

All in good time.

POOH: Christopher Robin, what day is it?

CHRISTOPHER ROBIN: It's today.

POOH: My favourite day.

Living in the moment at its finest.

BEING YOU

"Always be yourself."

—CHRISTOPHER ROBIN

Very Good Advice.

POOH: I don't feel very much like Pooh today.

PIGLET: There, there. I'll bring you tea and honey until you do.

Balloons help, too.

The wonderful thing
about tiggers is tiggers are
wonderful things. . . .
But the most wonderful
thing about tiggers is I'm
the only one.

—TIGGER

*Remember what's wonderful
about you.*

"I could spend a **happy** morning being Pooh."

—WINNIE THE POOH

Especially with a rousing game of Pooh Sticks!

ENDINGS

"Good-bye?
Oh, no, can't we go back to page one and do it all again?"

—WINNIE THE POOH

Why, of course, Pooh. Just flip back to the start!